The SPORTING WOMAN

The SPORTING WOMAN
A BOOK OF DAYS

PICTURE RESEARCH AND TEXT BY
SALLY FOX

BULFINCH PRESS
LITTLE, BROWN AND COMPANY
BOSTON   TORONTO   LONDON

DEDICATION

To all the women who enjoyed a challenge
and to the artists they inspired

Cover:
Tennis player
Cover for the magazine *Life*, August 5, 1915
Chromolithograph by John Labatta. American, 1915
Private collection

Title page:
Water duel
Hand-colored engraving. American, 1881
Private collection

First edition

ISBN 0-8212-1739-9

Bulfinch Press is an imprint and trademark of
Little, Brown and Company (Inc.)

Published simultaneously in Canada by
Little, Brown & Company (Canada) Limited

Printed in Italy

⬛ ACKNOWLEDGMENTS ⬛

I am deeply indebted to Serge Laget for enthusiastically and generously sharing his remarkable collection of materials that visually document the sporting woman.

Special thanks to the following, who were outstanding with their generous advice: Professor Saul Benison, University of Cincinnati Medical School; Robin Bledsoe, antiquarian bookseller; Mrs. Fumiko Cranston, Sackler Museum, Harvard University; Professor Scott Derrick, George Mason University; Mme. Monique Le Pelley Fonteny, Giraudon; Jean-Paul Mazot, coauthor with Françoise and Serge Laget of *Le Grand Livre du Sport Feminin;* Helene Roberts, Curator, Visual Collections, Fogg Museum, Harvard University; Professor Lynn Stephen, Northeastern University.

I am also grateful to the staffs of the following institutions who gave such sympathetic assistance: Bibliothèque Nationale, Paris; the British Museum; Cleveland Museum of Art; Documentation de la Réunion des Musées Nationaux; Kennedy Galleries; Los Angeles County Museum of Art; Metropolitan Museum of Art; Mount Holyoke College; Museum of Fine Arts, Boston; National Museum of American Art, Smithsonian Institution; New England Sports Museum; New-York Historical Society; New York Public Library; Smith College; The Strong Museum; Vassar College; Wellesley College; Yale Center for British Art. The research in France was made possible by the generous hospitality of Luisa Hirschbein.

Finally, I am especially grateful for the invaluable advice and encouragement of my brother, Will Lorin, my husband, Maury, and my sons, Jonathan, Gregory, and Michael.

The ₰PORTING WOMAN

"Women cheerfully share with men hardships, toil and endurance, climb mountains, sail on the seas, face wind and rain and the chill gusts of winter, as unconcernedly as they once followed their quiet occupations by their firesides. . . . It is scarcely necessary nowadays to offer an apology for sport. . . ."

—Lady Greville, equestrienne, 1894

Lady Greville, who loved the thrill of "a sharp, brisk gallop over turfy downs," was not alone. The spirit and adventure of sports have always challenged women—from ancient Egypt to Greece and Rome, from the Orient and Europe to the Americas. Works of art and popular visual materials of these cultures are valuable historical documents of women in sports, capturing the excitement and depicting the tools of the leisure activities of ordinary women. Since the sporting arena, however, has historically been the domain of men, how exceptional was the sporting woman?

Women's participation in sports was influenced by such factors as culture, social class, geography, and education. In all cultures, working-class women could expect only unending physical labor, but women of the leisure class have had both opportunity and latitude for personal expression in some kind of sport, since they could indulge themselves in appropriate equipment and dress and had access to the special settings for sports. Some of their pastimes, such as shooting or polo, were extremely demanding, requiring special training as well as natural skills, and they also served to expand the limits of the "feminine" world.

Pictures provide evidence that sporting women throughout history were not defeated by social constraints. The ancient Greek Olympic Games not only excluded women from competition, but even excluded them as spectators. Nevertheless, women did compete in the stadium at Olympia in non-Olympic years and received the same awards as their male counterparts: olive wreaths and the right to erect images of themselves. Their contests were a series of footraces, called the Heraia in honor of the goddess Hera, in which young, unmarried women sprinted 500 feet (160 meters), five-sixths of the distance normally run by men. Female athletes clearly could have run the entire course. Could it be that the shortened length was a reminder that women were not to be considered as competitors with men? After all, women had no role in Greek society other than motherhood. In Sparta, however, to ensure strong, healthy mothers to produce strong warriors, girls were trained and expected to compete in the same athletic games as boys.

The limits drawn for the sporting woman varied with time and place, but they were especially clear in the nineteenth century, when women, paradoxically, became increasingly interested in sports. As the Industrial Revolution created a growing middle class, more women had leisure time, but as in the past they were expected to be frail and dependent, and to remain indoors. Their primary role was motherhood, and their activities were expected to be limited to mild forms of exercise and sports such as lawn tennis and golf. Regardless of class, most sporting women were not expected to exhibit the characteristics associated with the male sporting world—strength, competitiveness, and the need to win. Nevertheless, some women rebelled against confinement and used sports to express their defiance and individuality.

The conventions of dress have often dictated women's sporting options. Though Plato recommended running and fencing for women in his ideal city, he believed they should wear "appropriate dress" for these sports after the age of thirteen. Until recently, the spirited sporting woman who committed herself to active sports like mountaineering, bicycling, hockey, tennis, and skating had to contend with "appropriate" but ungainly heavy skirts and corsets, sometimes crinolines and hats. Even by the turn of the twentieth century, fashion and "femininity" usually prevailed over comfort and efficiency. In golf, for example, despite the fact that women could make drives longer than eighty yards, ladies' golf links were often designed with short holes because "the posture and gestures required for a full swing are not particularly graceful when the player is clad in female dress" (Lord Moncrieff, 1902).

With the twentieth century, women used sports to redefine femininity. They encroached upon male preserves, such as hunting, risking censure by adopting some of the more comfortable male fashions. Such women were described as "not *brave* but *bold.*" In those sports that appeared *de novo* inspired by new inventions such as the bicycle, the motorcycle, the automobile, and the airplane, women immediately became active and unquestioned participants. Was this because there was no historical association with gender attached to these new mechanized sports?

The connection between health and exercise was personified by the athletic and educated "New Woman" emerging from the new women's colleges. However, in order to diminish any obvious challenge to the male world, women's college athletics were less demanding and kept secluded, in contrast to men's highly visible and profitable sports.

Activities that involved competition and physical contact were avoided as emulating men's sports too closely, resulting in inequities of space, money, and opportunity that persist to this day.

The pictures in this book, ranging from antiquity to 1930, are a visual tribute to the sporting woman's indomitable spirit throughout history, to her need to test her physical capabilities and to enjoy fulfilling her personal challenges, be they recreational or competitive. Looking at these images, one could ask a series of questions: Is the activity an individual or a team effort? Is it purely recreational, amateur or professional? What are the skills and how are they learned? Who determines standards and rules, and for whom are they designed? How competitive? How challenging? What are the satisfactions?

In spite of social pressures, there were always women whose spirit overcame fear of disapproval, such as the cricketer of 1875 who wrote:

"The knickerbockers bring comfort, the tunic confers respectability. It is a lovely thought that I can kick up my heels to my heart's content, and yet preserve decorum. As to what manner of female I look, I care nothing; my sensations are all I think about, and they are blissful."

Battledores and shuttlecock,
a forerunner of badminton, has been
popular in Asia for at least 2000 years.
Japanese women and children
traditionally played it on New Year's Day.

Women Playing with Shuttlecocks and Battledores by Yoshitoshi
Color on paper. Acc. no. M.84.31.53.5
Japanese, mid-nineteenth century
Los Angeles County Museum of Art

JANUARY

1

2

3

4

5

6

Ice yachting, also called ice sailing,
was the choice of women who were
both skilled and privileged, and who enjoyed
the heady sensation of speed.

Postcard
Chromolithograph by Jenny Nyström
Swedish, c.1900
Private collection

JANUARY

7

8

9

10

11

12

January
Fresco in the Castello del Buonsiglio, Trento
Italian, fourteenth century
Photo: Scala/Art Resource

snowball
fight
between
men and
women
in the
fourteenth
century.

JANUARY

13

14

15

16

17

18

This spirited skater of 1865 is wearing the "curled prow," the handmade wooden and metal skate designed exclusively for gliding that was in use from the 1780s to the 1870s.

JANUARY

19

20

21

22

23

24

Chromolithograph by Regnier after Calix
French, c.1865
Bibliothèque des Arts Décoratifs, Paris
Photo: Jean-Loup Charmet

Gymnastics, based on principles of mechanics and physiology, was believed to be as stimulating for women's minds as for their bodies.

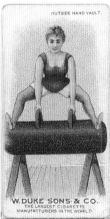

JANUARY

25

26

27

28

29

30
31

Cigarette insert cards
Chromolithographs
American, 1887
The Metropolitan Museum of Art, The Jefferson Burdick Collection

Fearless women enjoyed
the sensation of speed while
bobsledding and tobogganing
at resorts like Davos, Switzerland.

BOBSLEIGH ET TOBOGGAN

Mais c'est le toboggan et le
bobsleigh qui donnent les plus
enivrantes sensations de vitesse.
Ce n'est plus une glisse, c'est
un vol plané où l'on comprend
ce que peuvent sentir sur leurs
oiseaux les Farman et les
Wright.

FEBRUARY

1

2

3

4

5

6

Le Toboggan Sentimental, Davos, January 8, 1908 by René Lelong
Watercolor
French, 1908
Françoise and Serge Laget, Paris

FEBRUARY

7	
8	
9	
10	
11	
12	

By incorporating
physical education into their curricula,
women's colleges redefined "femininity"
to mean educated minds in
healthy bodies.

Cigar-box label
Embossed chromolithograph
American, c.1910
Collection John Grossman, The Gifted Line, Inc.

A respectable pastime
for middle-class women,
indoor bowling
quickly became a favorite
American sport.

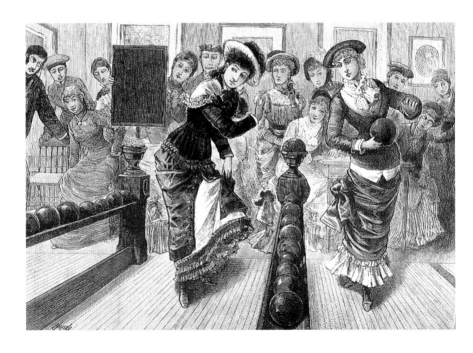

FEBRUARY

13

14

15

16

17

18

Frank Leslie's Illustrated Newspaper,
December 9, 1882
Hand-colored engraving
American, 1882
Private collection

Skate sailing originated in northern Europe and quickly spread to England and North America in the early 1900s. In this fast sport, speeds of more than 50 miles per hour have been recorded.

FEBRUARY

	19
	20
	21
	22
	23
	24

Cover by Victor Stroda for the magazine *Die Gartenlaube,* January 20, 1927
Painting
German, 1927
Private collection

S tag hunting on skis
in Nordic countries in the sixteenth
century was enjoyed by both
men and women.

Watercolor, sixteenth century
Bibliothèque Nationale, Paris
Photo: Jean-Loup Charmet

FEBRUARY

25

26

27

28

29

The first
women's international
ski race was held
at Chamonix
in 1908.

MARCH

	1
	2
	3
	4
	5
	6

Print by Edgar Bouilette (detail)
French, 1908
Photo: Mary Evans Picture Library, London

MARCH

7	
8	
9	
10	
11	
12	

Curling,
a Scottish winter sport
similar to bowling,
popular also in
northern Europe, Canada,
and the United States, was
played by middle-class
women in the early 1880s.

NEW STYLE OF CURLING FOR GIRLS.

A GAY PARTY OF YOUNG LADIES ENJOY THE SPORT OF CURLING ON THE ICE, CENTRAL PARK, NEW YORK.—See Page 10.

Hand-colored engraving, 1881
Private collection

Wrestling was a titillating spectator sport performed by women in music halls and theaters.

MARCH

13

14

15

16

17

18

Postcard
Embossed chromolithograph
French, before 1904
Private collection

This sixteenth-century Mughal miniature
depicts a queen and her women slaves playing polo,
a royal sport originating in Persia that flourished
in India throughout the Mughal dynasty.

MARCH

19

20

21

22

23

24

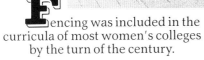

Fencing was included in the
curricula of most women's colleges
by the turn of the century.

MARCH

25

26

27

28

29

30
31

Chromolithograph by Joseph Tetlow
American, 1903
Private collection

Disregarding
inconvenient clothing, women
climbers confronted the eternal
challenge of the mountains
equipped only with
alpenstock and rope.

APRIL

1

2

3

4

5

6

Hand-colored engraving by George Defaine
French, c.1900
Françoise and Serge Laget, Paris

APRIL

7

8

9

10

11

12

FLYING TRAPEZE LEG FLY.

W. DUKE SONS & CO.
THE LARGEST CIGARETTE
MANUFACTURERS IN THE WORLD.

Using equipment
such as dumbbells and Indian
clubs, teachers of physical education,
especially Dio Lewis and Dudley Sargent,
devised systems of exercise and
gymnastics widely used
in schools.

Believed to have been played
by Mary, Queen of Scots, golf has always
been an approved and popular
"feminine" outdoor noncontact sport.

APRIL

13

14

15

16

17

18

Chromolithograph by Joseph Tetlow
American, 1903
Private collection

Cycling was born in 1868
when velocipedes, considered the first
real bicycles because of the pedals
attached to the front wheel axle,
were raced in France by women
as well as men.

Harper's Weekly, December 19, 1868
Hand-colored engraving
American, 1868
Private collection

APRIL

19

20

21

22

23

24

"The 'shooting lady' is now as much an established fact as her sister the 'hunting lady.' . . . Ladies who shoot, and who shoot well . . . are springing up on all sides. . . . "

—Lady Boynton, 1894

APRIL

	25
	26
	27
	28
	29
	30

Hand-colored print by Guydo
French, c.1890
Françoise and Serge Laget, Paris

"**T**he "New Woman" who wore "The Rational,"
also called "Bloomers" after its designer, Amelia Bloomer,
not only was more comfortable but also was
making a political statement.

MAY

1

2

3

4

5

6

nineteenth-century
illustration of Polynesian women
boxing on Tongatabu,
one of the "Friendly Islands"
named by Captain Cook.

Voyage autour de Monde. Tonga-tabou
Hand-colored engraving. Printer: Drouart, Paris
French, nineteenth century
Françoise and Serge Laget, Paris

MAY

7

8

9

10

11

12

To fly in 1922, whether as pilot or as passenger,
this woman had to have a sporting spirit.

MAY

13

14

15

16

17

18

Gazette du Bon Ton, Number 4, 1922, plate 27
Pochoir
French, 1922
Bibliothèque des Arts Décoratifs, Paris

MAY

19
20
21
22
23
24

Hand-colored engraving published by T. Tegg
English, 1819
Bibliothèque des Arts Décoratifs, Paris
Photo: Jean-Loup Charmet

"**T**he hobby-horse," also called "'The Ladies Accelerator," was one of the first bicycles and allowed women to propel themselves while fashionably dressed.

Archery, a favorite
open-air sport of fashionable women,
was always considered a "feminine"
sport of skill suitable for both
married and single women.

25

26

27

28

29

30
31

The Fair Toxophilites (English Archers, Nineteenth Century) by William Powell Frith
Oil on canvas
English, 1872
The Royal Albert Memorial Museum and Art Gallery, Exeter
Photo: Bridgeman/Giraudon

A women's motor tricycle race at Longchamps in 1899.

L'IMPARTIAL
DE L'EST
Supplément Illustré
du Dimanche 18 Juin 1899.

N° 25.

Administration : 71, rue Saint-Dizier
NANCY

Paraît chaque semaine

Une fête sportive à Longchamp
La course de motocycles des artistes de Paris

JUNE

1

2

3

4

5

6

Cover by Alphonse Pronier
for the magazine *L'Impartial,* June 18, 1899
French, 1899
Françoise and Serge Laget, Paris

JUNE

7

8

9

10

11

12

A trained acrobatic dancer from Egypt performing a somersault.

Painting on limestone fragment
Egyptian, New Kingdom, XVIII dynasty, 1567–1320 B.C.
Egyptian Museum, Turin
Photo: John G. Ross/Madeline Grimaldi

A "smock race,"
a footrace run by women in
chemises, with a smock and a leg of mutton
as prizes, was one of the few sports poor women
participated in at English country fairs at the
end of the eighteenth century.

1811 by Tho.s Tegg N.o 111 Cheapside

JUNE

13

14

15

16

17

18

Rural Sports, Smock Racing by Thomas Rowlandson (detail)
Hand-colored etching published by T. Tegg
English, 1811
Houghton Library, Harvard University, Cambridge

JUNE

19
20
21
22
23
24

These rakish women demonstrate trick billiard shots beneath the group portrait of the manufacturers of the billiard table.

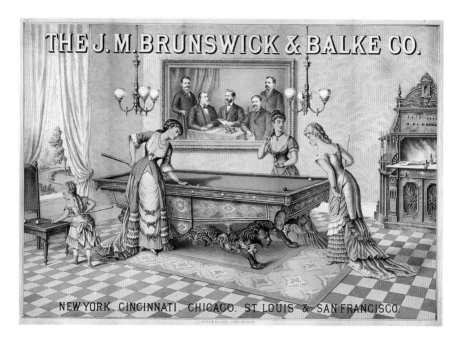

Poster for the J.M. Brunswick & Balke Company
Chromolithograph by Kurz & Allison, Chicago
American, c.1885
The New-York Historical Society, Bella C. Landauer Collection of Advertising Art

Women's ability to drive the newly invented automobile was not questioned.

"The Drive," after a painting by J. L. Stewart
Cover for the magazine *L'Illustré soleil du dimanche*, October 20, 1901
French, 1901
Françoise and Serge Laget, Paris

JUNE

25

26

27

28

29

30

Played in Europe
for centuries, badminton was
recommended to young women as
a pleasant pastime and healthy
exercise by the end of the
eighteenth century.

JULY

1

2

3

4

5

6

Hand-colored engraving
French, late eighteenth–early nineteenth century
Françoise and Serge Laget, Paris

和田の春
八十漁く
紀路を
虹ね
人みは
はけま
あまの
ほり舟

A noncompetitive sport,
fishing was socially acceptable
as a relaxation for women in both
Eastern and Western cultures.

JULY

7

8

9

10

11

12

JULY

13
14
15
16
17
18

For centuries, women swam either in the nude or in a long, loose, sacklike bathing dress. Specific clothing for swimming did not appear until the nineteenth century.

Girls bathing by Bernadino Luini
Fresco transferred to canvas
Italian, 1520–1523
Brera Gallery, Milan

JULY

19

20

21

22

23

24

Cover by Albert Sebille for the magazine *Les Sports Modernes*, April 1906
French, 1906
Françoise and Serge Laget, Paris

LES SPORTS MODERNES

Women of leisure enjoyed racing
the newly invented motorboat.

Egyptian
woman
swimmer.

JULY

	25
	26
	27
	28
	29
	30 31

Wooden statuette
Egyptian, New Kingdom, XVIII dynasty, 1567–1320 B.C.
National Maritime Museum, Haifa
Photo: Erich Lessing, Magnum Photos

This women's cricket match, which took place in 1811, lasted three days.

Rural Sports or a Cricket Match Extraordinary by Thomas Rowlandson
Hand-colored etching published by T. Tegg
English, 1811–1812
The British Museum, London

AUGUST

1

2

3

4

5

6

AUGUST

7

8

9

10

11

12

The "Annette Kellerman," the revolutionary one-piece bathing suit exposing and freeing arms and legs, was named for the celebrated exhibition swimmer who introduced it just after World War I.

AUGUST

13

14

15

16

17

18

In the 1870s
lawn tennis quickly replaced
croquet as the most popular sport
for women, who played enthusiastically
in spite of their unsuitable
fashions.

Women have flown in hot-air balloons
since they were invented in France in 1783.
This print documents the second ascent of
Citizeness Henri together with Citizen Garnerin
in 1798, the sixth year of the Republic.

AUGUST

19

20

21

22

23

24

AUGUST

25

26

27

28

29

30
31

Now popularly called "The Bikini Girls," these Roman gymnasts have been preserved in mosaic since the fourth century A.D.

Mosaic, Piazza Armerina, Sicily
Roman, fourth century A.D.
Photo: Scala/Art Resource

The need of poor rural women everywhere for active exercise and recreation is illustrated in this mid-nineteenth-century Russian print.

SEPTEMBER

1

2

3

4

5

6

Hand-colored engraving
Russian, mid-nineteenth century
Bibliothèque des Arts Décoratifs, Paris
Photo: Jean-Loup Charmet

Cover for *Le Figaro Illustré*, July 1890
Chromolithograph
French, 1890
Private collection

By 1890 rowing was
an established sport for European
as well as American college women,
and rowing equipment was sold to both
men and women as exercise machines
for the home.

SEPTEMBER

7

8

9

10

11

12

SEPTEMBER

13

14

15

16

17

18

Croquet, a fashionable garden-party recreation mixing mild exercise and flirtation, was most popular in the 1860s and 1870s.

This polo player demonstrates
one of the most difficult strokes, a forehand
shot from the left side of the horse.

SEPTEMBER

	19
	20
	21
	22
	23
	24

Cover by Coles Phillips for the magazine *Life*, September 1, 1927
American, 1927
Private collection

Women of the Santee Dakota tribe from Wisconsin played doubleball, a vigorous and complicated game related to lacrosse, occasionally using as many as forty women on a team.

25

26

27

28

29

30

Ball-play of the women, Prairie du Chien, by George Catlin
American, 1835–36
Oil on canvas, 19½" × 27⅝"
National Museum of American Art, Smithsonian Institution, Washington, D.C., gift of Mrs. Joseph Harrison, Jr.

OCTOBER

1

2

3

4

5

6

AMAZON HURDLE-   RACE.

By the turn of the century,
skilled horsewomen wore trousers underneath
their skirts, bowler hats, and habits with
a trimmer, more masculine cut.

Print after a painting by Ludwig Koch
German, 1909
Photo: Mary Evans Picture Library, London

By 1923 not only were women's soccer teams competing internationally, the team members were wearing shorts.

OCTOBER

7

8

9

10

11

12

Cover for the magazine *Le Petit Journal,* November 18, 1923
French, 1923
Françoise and Serge Laget, Paris

Hunting was a
serious pursuit of Indian royal ladies,
as depicted in this realistic nineteenth-century miniature.

OCTOBER

13

14

15

16

17

18

Palace Ladies Hunting from a Pavilion
Miniature painting, Rajasthani, Kotah School
Indian, c.1810
The Cleveland Museum of Art, Purchase from the J. H. Wade Fund, 55.48

OCTOBER

19

20

21

22

23

24

Cover for the magazine *La Mode du Jour*, July 6, 1893
French, 1893
Françoise and Serge Laget, Paris

The first tandem, a side-by-side called "The Sociable," was difficult to maneuver because of the bicycle's width and the head winds.

OCTOBER

25

26

27

28

29

30
31

Bronze statue
Greek, 520 B.C.
British Museum, London
Photo: Michael Holford, London

This small bronze of a Spartan girl runner, from the lid of a vase, is one of the few Greek artworks depicting women athletes.

This "New Woman" had the courage
not only to enjoy a masculine sport, game shooting,
but also to adopt men's more comfortable
and appropriate sports clothes.

Trade card
Chromolithograph
American, c.1900
Private collection

NOVEMBER

1

2

3

4

5

6

"**F**ootball is such good form, you know."
The caption for this 1894 print obviously refers to the
attractive feminine players, as well as to the sport.

NOVEMBER

7

8

9

10

11

12

Print by W. Granville Smith from *Truth*
American, 1894
Françoise and Serge Laget, Paris

NOVEMBER

13

14

15

16

17

18

Cover by Mark Rutherford for *Ainslee's* magazine, November 1899
American, 1899
Courtesy Kennedy Galleries, Inc., New York

This eye-catching magazine cover seems to make the subversive suggestion that a woman could and would play the definitive masculine sport, football.

Introduced into the
United States from England in
1901, field hockey quickly became
the most popular outdoor team
sport of young American women.

Print
English (?), 1912
Photo: Mary Evans Picture Library

NOVEMBER

19

20

21

22

23

24

The intense concentration, the masculine cut of her coat, and the powder horn identify this eighteenth-century "lady shooter" as a serious sportswoman.

The Ladies Shooting Poney by John Collet
Hand-colored mezzotint
English, 1780
Yale Center for British Art, Paul Mellon Collection, New Haven

NOVEMBER

	25
	26
	27
	28
	29
	30

The enthusiasm of women college students for basketball persisted in spite of the "girls' rules" of 1897, designed to diminish the rough physical contact inherent in "boys' rules."

DECEMBER

1

2

3

4

5

6

Chromolithograph by Joseph Tetlow
American, 1903
Private collection

Snowshoeing,
first a necessary activity of Eskimo
and North American Indian trappers,
hunters, and travelers, became an
organized sport in Canada
in the 1840s.

DECEMBER

7

8

9

10

11

12

Billiards, introduced from England into
France by Louis XIV, was a fashionable
sport of the nobility by the end of
the seventeenth century.

Hand-colored engraving by N. Arnoult
French, seventeenth century
Private collection
Photo: Jean-Loup Charmet

DECEMBER

13

14

15

16

17

18

A craze for roller skating, which appealed to all classes, had swept Western Europe and the United States by 1885.

DECEMBER

19

20

21

22

23

24

Men and women
throwing snowballs in the fifteenth century.

DECEMBER

25

26

27

28

29

30
31

Les Heures de la Duchesse de Bourgogne. December
Ms 76/1362, fol. 12v
French, c.1450
Musée Condé, Chantilly
Photo: Giraudon / Art Resource

SELECTED BIBLIOGRAPHY &

Adrian, Marlene J. *Sports Women*. Medicine and Sport Science, vol. 24. Basel: S. Karger AG, 1987.

Arlott, John, and Arthur Daley. *Pageantry of Sport: From the Age of Chivalry to the Age of Victoria*. New York: Hawthorne Books, 1968.

Baillie-Grohman, William A. *Sport in Art: Iconography of Sport: During Four Hundred Years from the Beginning of the Fifteenth to the End of the Eighteenth Centuries*. London: Ballantyne & Co., Ltd., 1913.

Banta, Martha. *Imaging American Women: Idea and Ideals in Cultural History*. New York: Columbia University Press, 1987.

Bloodgood, Lida Fleitmann. *The Saddle of Queens: The Story of the Side-saddle*. London: J. A. Allen & Co., 1959.

Boutilier, Mary A., and Lucinda SanGiovanni. *The Sporting Woman*. Champaign, IL: Human Kinetics Publishers, 1983.

Butler, A. J. *Sport in Classic Times*. New York: E. P. Dutton & Co., 1930.

Casteras, Susan P. *Images of Victorian Womanhood in English Art*. Cranbury, NJ: Associated University Presses, 1987.

Cunnington, Phillis, and Alan Mansfield. *English Costume for Sports and Outdoor Recreation: From the Sixteenth to the Nineteenth Centuries*. London: Adam and Charles Black, 1969.

Deuchar, Stephen. *Noble Exercise: The Sporting Ideal in Eighteenth-Century British Art*. New Haven: Yale Center for British Art, 1982.

Dijkstra, Bram. *Idols of Perversity: Fantasies of Feminine Evil in Fin-de-Siècle Culture*. New York and Oxford: Oxford University Press, 1986.

Elias, Norbert, and Eric Dunning. *Quest for Excitement: Sport and Leisure in the Civilizing Process*. Oxford and New York: Basil Blackwell, 1986.

Gardiner, E. Norman. *Athletics of the Ancient World*. Oxford: Clarendon Press, 1955.

Glubok, Shirley, and Alfred Tamarin. *Ancient Games in Ancient Greece*. New York: Harper & Row, 1976.

Goldman, Paul. *Sporting Life: An Anthology of British Sporting Prints*. London: British Museum Publications, Ltd., 1983.

Green, Harvey. *Fit for America: Health, Fitness, Sport, and American Society*. New York: Pantheon Books, 1986.

Greville, Lady. *Ladies in the Field: Sketches of Sport*. New York: D. Appleton & Co., 1894.

Guttmann, Allen. *A Whole New Ball Game: An Interpretation of American Sports*. Chapel Hill, NC, and London: University of North Carolina Press, 1988.

Harris, H. A. *Sport in Greece and Rome*. Ithaca, NY: Cornell University Press, 1972.

Howell, Reet. *Her Story in Sport: A Historical Anthology of Women in Sport*. West Point, NY: Leisure Press, 1982.

Laget, Françoise and Serge, and Jean-Paul Mazot. *Le Grand Livre du Sport Feminin*. Belleville-sur-Saone: FMT Editions, Sigefa, 1982.

Mangan, J. A., and Roberta J. Park. *From 'Fair Sex' to Feminism: Sport and the Socialization of Women in the Industrial and Post-Industrial Eras*. London: Frank Cass & Co., Ltd., 1987.

PICTURE CREDITS FOR DETAILS

Page 1: Private collection

Opposite title page: Library of Congress

Copyright page: Manesse Codex, Cod. Pal. Germ. 848, f. 26, Universitätsbibliothek, Heidelberg (Photo: Mary Evans Picture Library, London)

Introduction: Bibliothèque des Arts Décoratifs, Paris (Photo: Jean-Loup Charmet); Françoise and Serge Laget, Paris; National Railway Museum, York, England

Jan. 1: Bibliothèque des Arts Décoratifs, Paris (Photo: Jean-Loup Charmet)

Mar. 1: Françoise and Serge Laget, Paris

Mar. 25: Margaret Woodbury Strong Museum, Rochester

Apr. 7: The Metropolitan Museum of Art, The Jefferson Burdick Collection

May 13: Private collection

June 13: Private collection

July 1: Private collection

Sept. 7: James R. Bakkar Antiques, Inc., Cambridge, MA (Photo: Heider Studios)

Oct. 1: Private collection

Nov. 1: Margaret Woodbury Strong Museum, Rochester

Dec. 25: Manesse Codex, Cod. Pal. Germ. 848, f. 26, Universitätsbibliothek, Heidelberg (Photo: Mary Evans Picture Library, London)

Colophon page: Private collection (Photo: Jean-Loup Charmet)

Bibliography continued:

Michener, James. *Sports in America*. New York: Random House, 1976.

Mrozek, Donald J. *Sport and American Mentality 1880–1910*. Knoxville, TN: University of Tennessee Press, 1983.

Sport in Art. Catalogue of exhibition organized by Bruckmann Stistung, Munich, 1972.

Stow, Hester Harrington. *Greek Athletics and Festivals in the Fifth Century*. Boston: Division of Museum Extension, Museum of Fine Arts, 1939.

Swaddling, Judith. *The Ancient Olympic Games*. Austin, TX: University of Texas Press, 1984.

Sweet, Waldo E. *Sport and Recreation in Ancient Greece*. New York and Oxford: Oxford University Press, 1987.

Twin, Stephanie L. *Out of the Bleachers: Writings on Women and Sport*. Old Westbury, NY: The Feminist Press; New York: McGraw-Hill Co., 1979.

Yalouris, Nicolaos. *The Eternal Olympics*. New Rochelle, NY: Caratzas Bros., 1979.

Copyedited by Betsy Pitha

Designed by Rick Horton

Production coordination by Amanda Wicks Freymann

Composition in ITC Garth Graphic and Futura Light by Composing Room of New England

Color separations, printing, and binding by Mondadori, Verona, Italy